My First ORIGAMI Fun

igloobooks

Contents

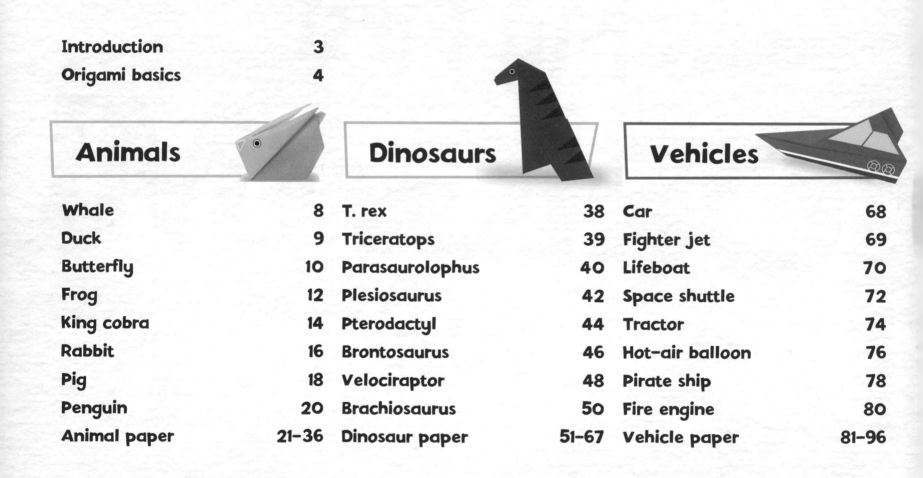

Difficulty Key

Easy ⭐

Medium ⭐⭐

Hard ⭐⭐⭐

Introduction

With this First Origami Fun book you have everything you need to create your own awesome animals, ferocious dinosaurs and cool vehicles. There is no glue needed!

Each section has clear, step-by-step instructions and pictures, as well as a difficulty rating to show if a model is easy, medium or hard. Before you get started, read the guide on page 4 to help master the basic folds of origami.

When you are ready to make your first model, pick an animal, dinosaur or vehicle and find the matching paper at the end of each section. Carefully cut the paper out of your book.

Start by making some of the easier models first, then move on to the more complicated designs as you get more confident. When your first origami model is finished, use the stickers to decorate it, then press out one of the four backgrounds to really set the scene!

Origami basics

Where does origami come from?

Origami is the traditional Japanese art of folding paper to make shapes, and it is an incredible 2,000 years old! The word origami literally means fold (oru) paper (kami).

Awesome origami facts!

- The smallest origami model in the world was made using a 1 mm x 1 mm square of paper, a microscope and a very steady pair of hands!

- According to an ancient Japanese legend, anyone who makes 1,000 origami cranes will be granted a wish.

- Sweet wrappers have been weaved into handbags, belts and hats using origami.

- Edible origami can be made from wonton wrappers (a dough which is as thin as paper).

Paper-folding techniques

Learning how to fold paper in different ways will help you to make all sorts of interesting shapes and designs.

Start by folding your paper square in half. Take one corner point and fold it over exactly to meet the opposite corner. This will make a triangle shape. Make sure your fold line is crisp

Use scrap paper to practise this super-simple fold, as well as the folds shown on the next tw pages, before starting your first origami projec

Most models in this book can be created just by folding the paper, but a few require scissors. Look out for this symbol throughout the book to see when scissors are needed.

Scissors needed!
Ask an adult to help you

Finally, each set of instructions has a paper symbol, so you can find the correct piece of paper to use.

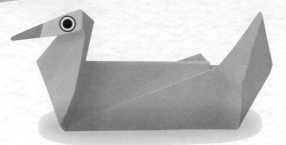

The language of origami

The symbols below describe the different types of folds and instructions used in origami models. You will see these symbols throughout the book, so it is a good idea to practise each one before you get going.

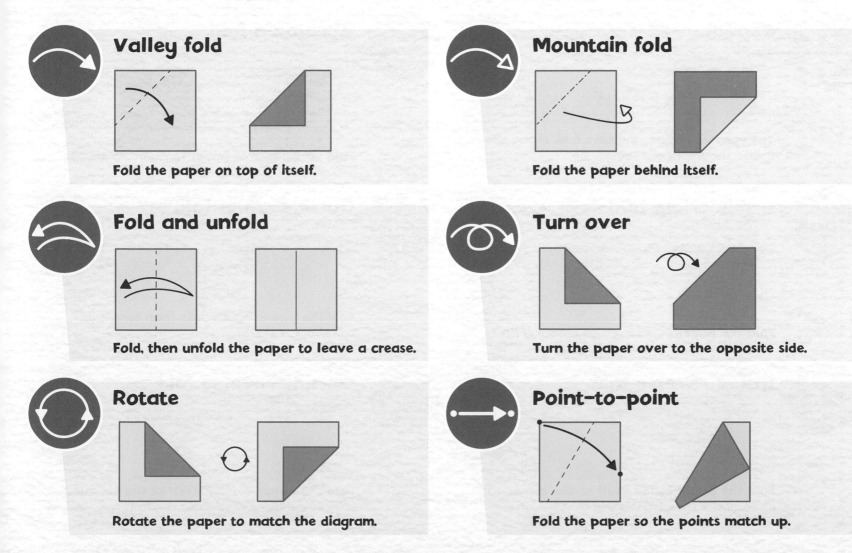

Valley fold
Fold the paper on top of itself.

Mountain fold
Fold the paper behind itself.

Fold and unfold
Fold, then unfold the paper to leave a crease.

Turn over
Turn the paper over to the opposite side.

Rotate
Rotate the paper to match the diagram.

Point-to-point
Fold the paper so the points match up.

Squash fold

 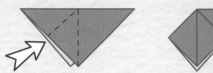

Open the flap and re-fold downwards.

Pull

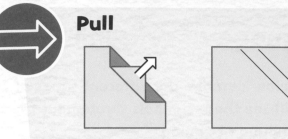

Pull the paper back after folding.

Repeat

The number of lines indicate how many times a fold should be repeated.

Accordion fold

Fold each layer of paper to create a zigzag.

Inside crimp fold

 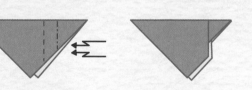

Fold the paper in on itself to create a pleat.

Outside crimp fold

Fold the paper backwards, then forwards to create a zigzag.

Inside reverse fold

Fold the paper inside itself at the crease to change the direction of the flap.

Outside reverse fold

Fold the paper outside itself at the crease to change the direction of the flap.

Animals

Whale

Make a splash by creating your very own whale...
but remember, he is not waterproof!

⭐

1 Fold and unfold the paper in half to make a crease.

2 Fold the top and bottom points into the middle.

3 Fold the front of the kite shape inwards to meet the middle crease.

4 Fold the entire shape in half, from bottom to top along the main crease edge.

5 Now bend the pointy end upwards behind the body to make the tail.

6 Add stickers from your sticker sheet and your whale is complete!

"Spurt!"

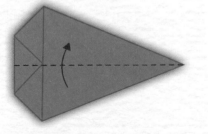

8

Duck

This cute little duck is so easy to make, you'll go quackers over it!

1 Follow steps 1 and 2 from the whale origami to create a kite shape.

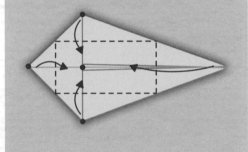

2 Fold each point of the kite shape in on itself to make a rectangle.

3 Fold the large triangle on the right in half. This will make the neck and head.

4 Fold the whole shape in half behind itself along the main crease edge.

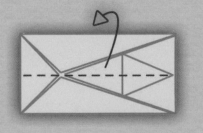

5 Gently pull both the triangle shapes from each end upwards to make a neck, beak and tail.

6 Add stickers from your sticker sheet and then you are done.

"Quack!"

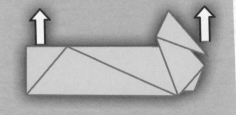

Butterfly

Follow the steps below to create a beautiful butterfly. This also looks great when using old wrapping paper.

★ ★

1 Fold and unfold the paper horizontally to make a crease.

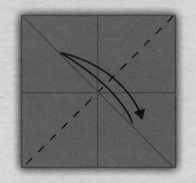

2 Fold and unfold the paper vertically.

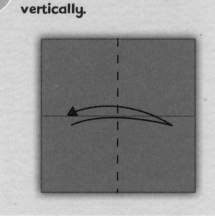

3 Fold and unfold the paper diagonally to make a crease.

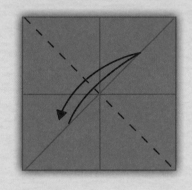

4 Fold and unfold the paper on the opposite diagonal.

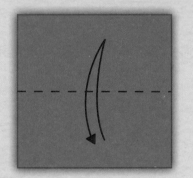

5 Push the sides inwards so the shape folds along the horizontal crease.

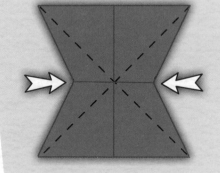

6 Squash the top down so the whole shape is flattened into a triangle shape.

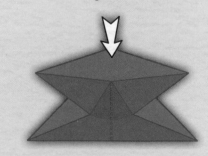

7 Fold the top flaps on each side up to the top tip, as shown below.

8 Turn the paper over and rotate it 180 degrees so the tip is pointing down.

180°

9 Fold the tip of the top flap up so that it peeks just above the top fold.

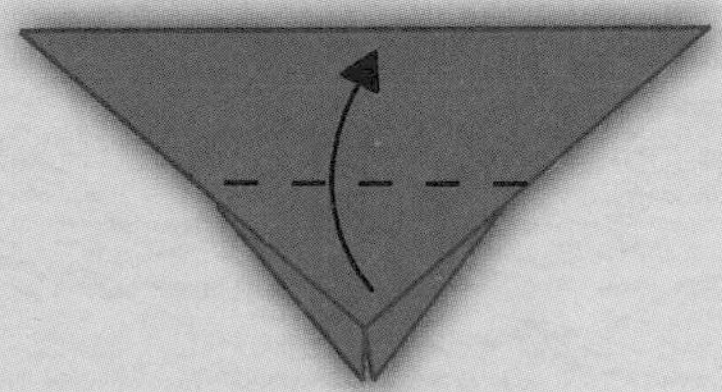

10 Squash the flaps at the sides, then fold the tip behind itself.

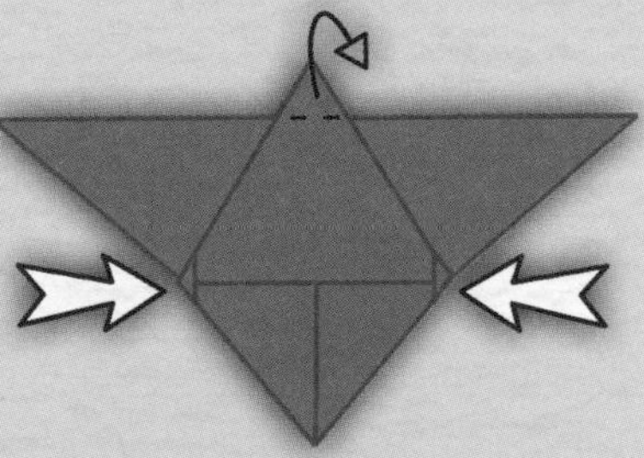

11 Pinch the crease in the middle so the butterfly wings stand out.

12 Decorate your butterfly with stickers from your sticker sheet, and it's ready to flutter away!

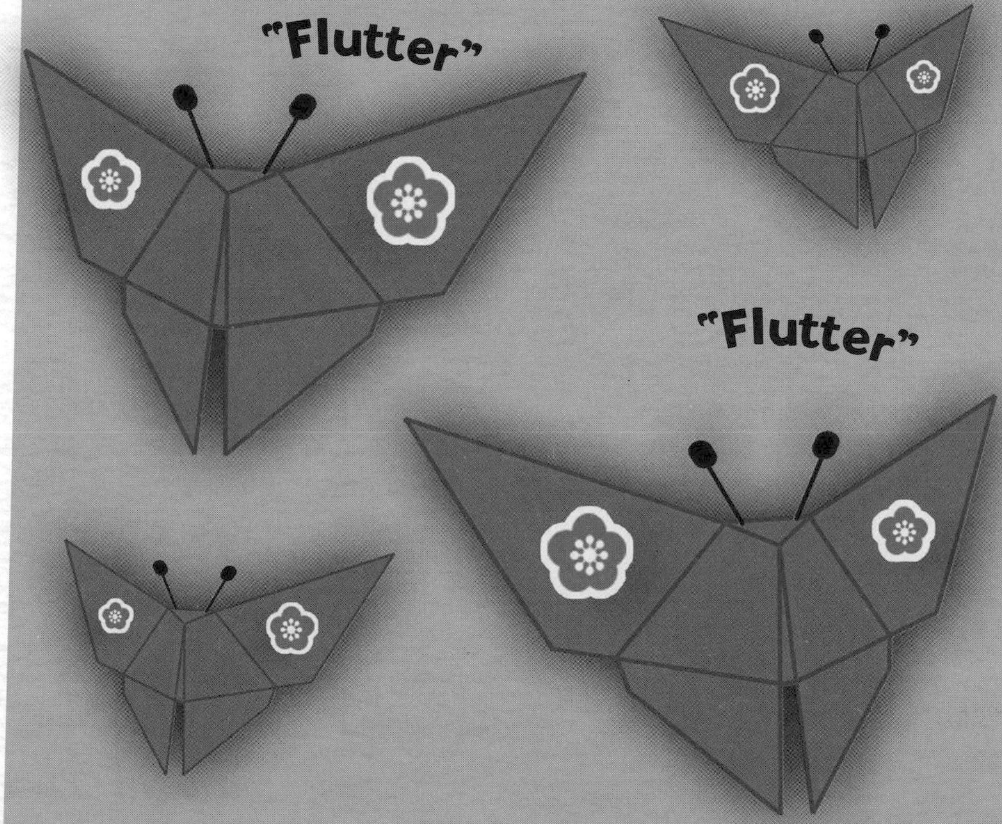

"Flutter"

"Flutter"

Frog

Croak-croak! Fold up your patterned paper to make your own little bouncing friend.

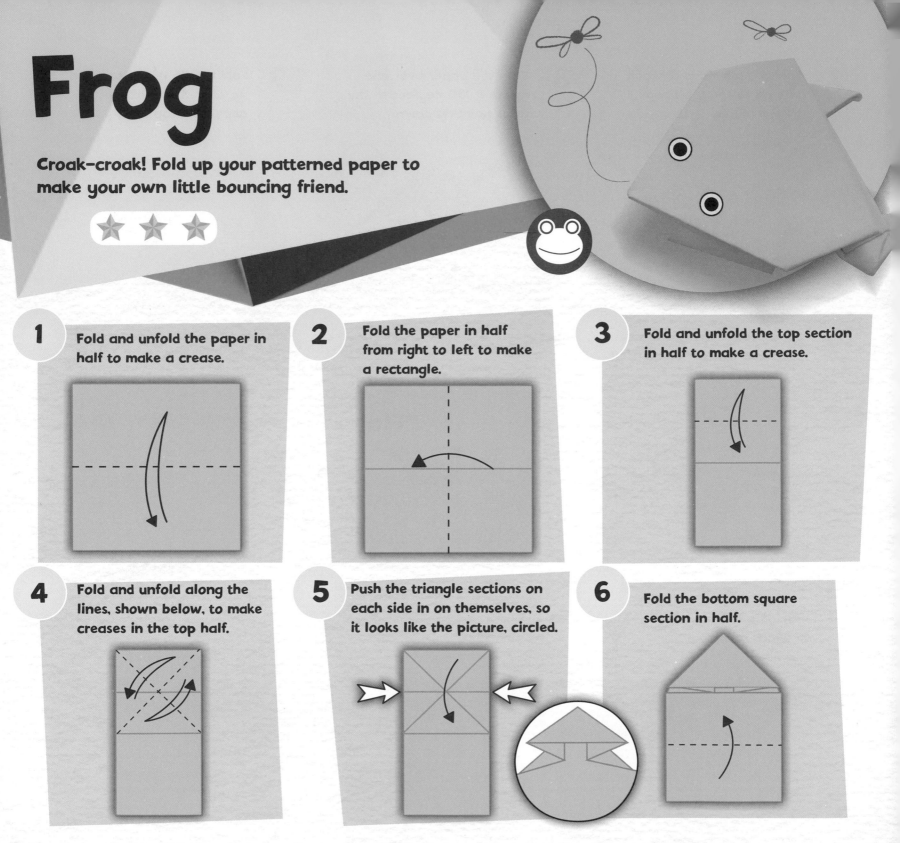

1 Fold and unfold the paper in half to make a crease.

2 Fold the paper in half from right to left to make a rectangle.

3 Fold and unfold the top section in half to make a crease.

4 Fold and unfold along the lines, shown below, to make creases in the top half.

5 Push the triangle sections on each side in on themselves, so it looks like the picture, circled.

6 Fold the bottom square section in half.

7 Lift the top flap of the triangle and fold the bottom rectangle inwards to meet in the middle and form an arrow shape.

8 Fold up the bottom square section in half, as shown.

9 Fold and unfold at the corners to make diagonal creases.

10 Pull the inner sections under the triangle out to the sides, then push inwards.

11 Fold along the lines shown below to create 4 triangles (see step 12). These are the legs.

12 Fold the paper shape upwards and in half.

13 Fold the top half back on itself. The paper will be thick so press hard to make a crease.

14 Turn the shape over then add eye stickers from your sticker sheet to really bring your frog to life!

"Ribbit-ribbit!" "Ribbit-ribbit!"

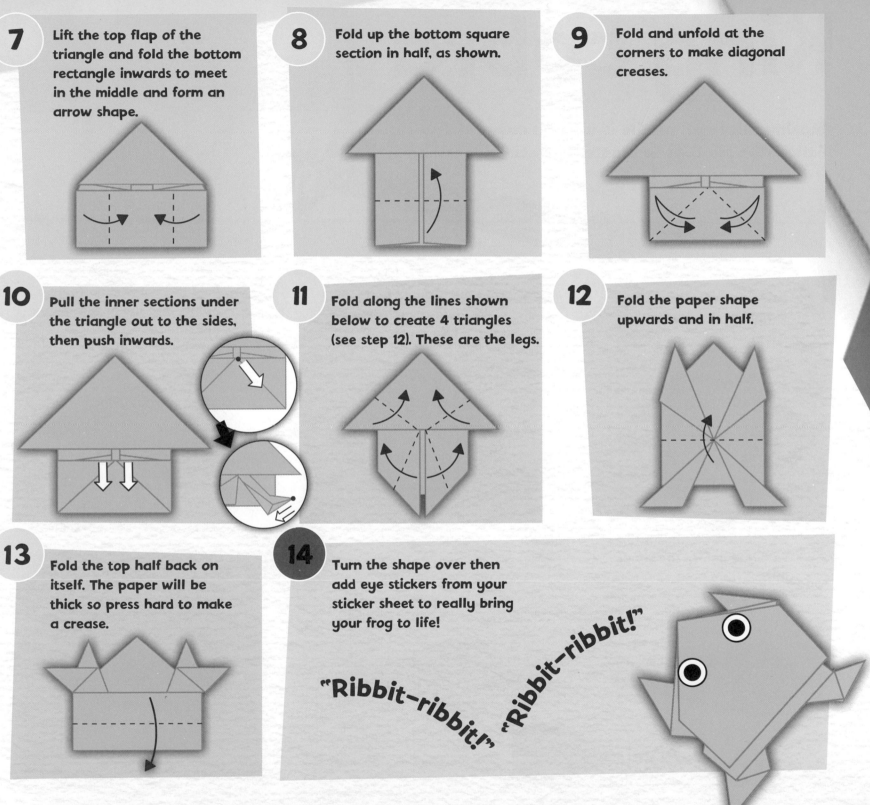

King cobra

Making this royal reptile is fun and easy.
Follow the sss-teps to create your sss-uper sss-nake.

1 Fold and unfold the paper in half to make a crease.

2 Fold the top and bottom points into the middle to form a kite shape.

3 Fold the top and bottom points into the middle once more.

4 Fold and unfold the shape in half from right to left to make a crease in the middle.

5 Fold the tip of the kite inwards to meet the edges of the folded paper.

6 Fold the left section outwards behind itself.

7 Fold the tail inwards so the point is at the middle crease.

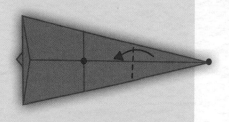

8 Fold the tail back on itself creating an 's' shape.

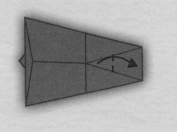

9 Stand your shape up on the base of the structure.

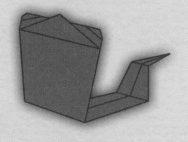

10 Pull the front section towards you so that it bends at a 90 degree angle. This is the head.

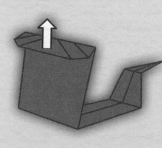

11 Pinch the front section downwards to make a 'v' shape for the eyes.

12 Add the finishing touches to your snake by using stickers from your sticker sheet.

"HISSS!"

15

Rabbit

Make your own adorable fluffy bunny using the paper provided. Hop to it!

Scissors needed!
Ask an adult to help you

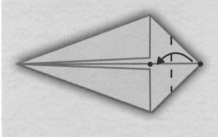

1 Fold and unfold the paper in half to make a crease.

2 Fold the top and bottom points into the middle to form a kite shape.

3 Fold the tip of the kite in to meet the edges of the folded paper at the middle point.

4 Fold the tip back on itself creating an 's' shape, making sure the tip goes past the edge. This will be the tail.

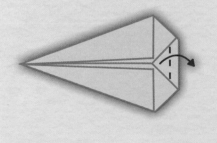

5 You should now have a shape that looks like the picture below.

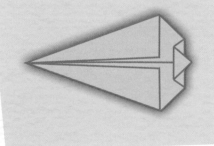

6 Turn the paper over and fold the tip to meet the top edge.

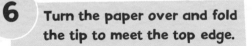

7 Fold the shape in half, behind itself.

8 Pull up the tip of the triangle and squash down the left edge to create a new crease.

9 Use scissors to cut down the middle of the triangle to create the ears.

10 Pull the ears out to the side so your figure stands up.

11 Add some stickers from your sticker sheet and your bunny is ready to bounce!

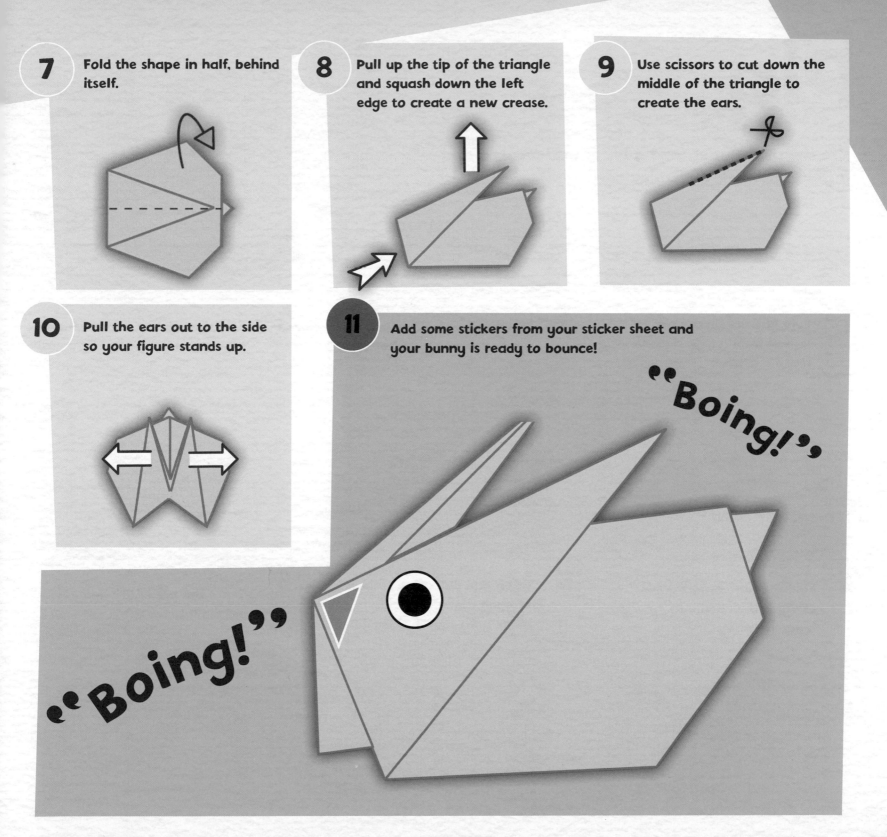

"Boing!"

"Boing!"

17

Pig

Use the pink paper (and a bit of patience) to fold a perfect piglet. Oink, oink!

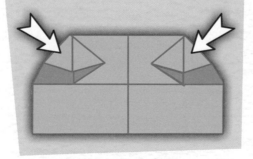

1 Fold and unfold the paper in half from left to right to make a crease.

2 Fold and unfold the paper in half from top to bottom.

3 Fold the top and bottom edges down to meet the middle crease.

4 Fold the top corners down towards the middle to create creases.

5 Open and pull up the middles of each triangle you have just made then squash them down.

6 Rotate the paper 180 degrees and repeat step 4.

180°

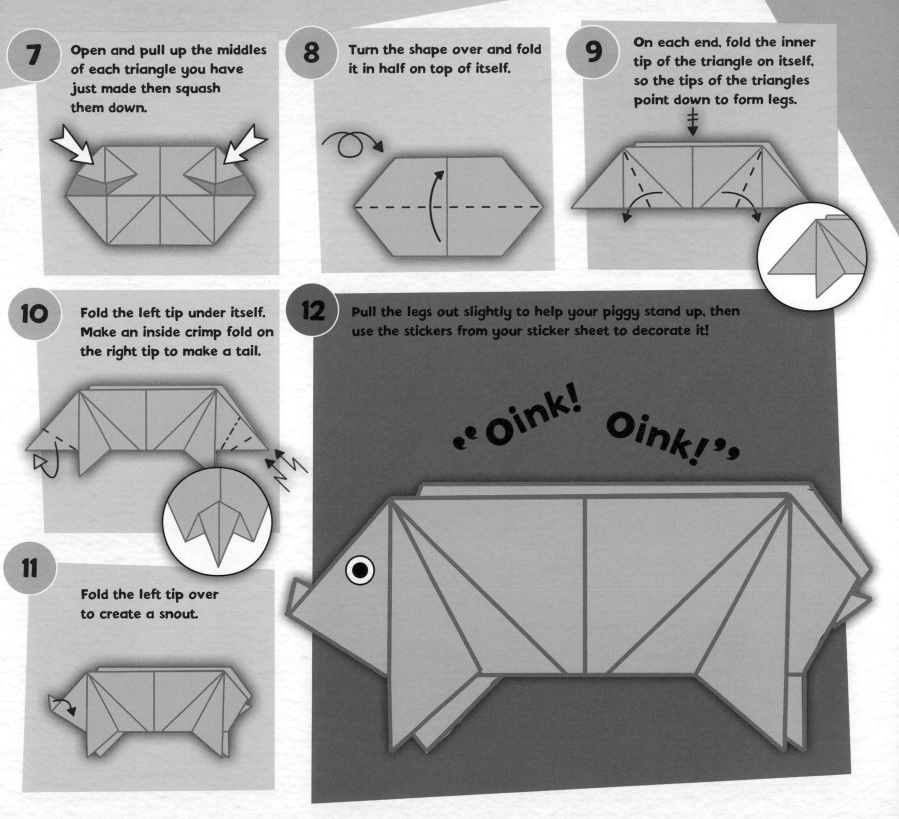

7 Open and pull up the middles of each triangle you have just made then squash them down.

8 Turn the shape over and fold it in half on top of itself.

9 On each end, fold the inner tip of the triangle on itself, so the tips of the triangles point down to form legs.

10 Fold the left tip under itself. Make an inside crimp fold on the right tip to make a tail.

11 Fold the left tip over to create a snout.

12 Pull the legs out slightly to help your piggy stand up, then use the stickers from your sticker sheet to decorate it!

"Oink! Oink!"

19

Penguin

Pick up some paper and fold this cool little penguin.

1 Fold and unfold the paper in half to make a crease, then fold the left and right points into the middle to make a wide kite shape.

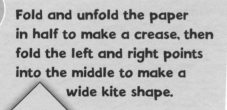

2 Fold the top down so the tip meets the point shown below.

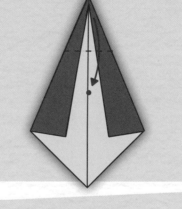

3 Turn the shape over and fold the bottom tip up as shown.

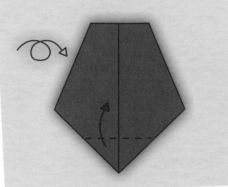

4 Fold the shape in half, from left to right.

5 Stand your penguin up and decorate him with stickers from your sticker sheet.

"Waddle!"

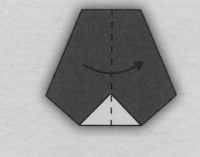

20

Dinosaurs

T. rex

T. rex is so famous for a reason – he was terrifying!
Luckily this model is not as scary as the real thing...

Easy ⭐

1 Fold the paper in half to make a crease. Fold the top and bottom edges to the middle to make a kite shape.

2 Turn the shape over and fold the right side back to the left to make the first crease. Then fold the pointed flap to the right to make an accordion fold.

3 Fold the shape in half along the main crease line, so that the fold is at the bottom.

4 To make the neck, bring the left point upwards so that the fold goes inside, making a reverse fold.

180°

5 Turn the shape over. Fold the point back to make the head shape. Fold the edges back in line with the main body shape.

6 Add the stickers from your sticker sheet to give T. rex a ferocious look!

"Raah!"

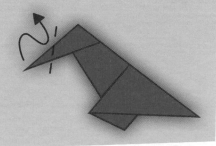

Triceratops

Have three times the fun with this hard-hitting, three-horned, happy chappy.

Easy  ⭐

1 Fold and unfold the paper left to right. Repeat from right to left, making a triangle.

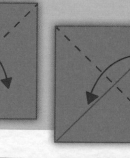

2 Fold the bottom left tip up to the right edge to meet the point as shown below.

3 Fold the shape back on itself along the middle crease.

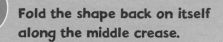

4 Make an outside reverse fold on the left tip to create the nose and horn shape.

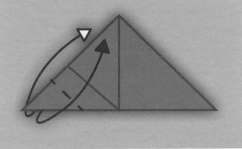

5 Fold the right tip towards itself, as shown below to make a tail.

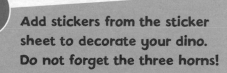

6 Add stickers from the sticker sheet to decorate your dino. Do not forget the three horns!

"Bomp!"

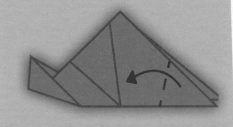

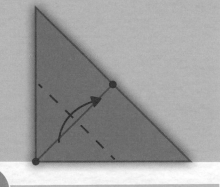

39

Parasaurolophus

Make this dinosaur which was known for its strange-shaped head!

Hard ⭐⭐⭐

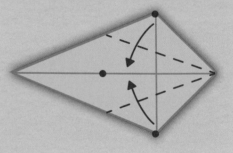

1 Fold and unfold the paper in half from top to bottom to make a crease.

2 Fold the top and bottom points into the middle to make a kite shape.

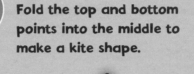

3 Fold the top and bottom points into the centre, to make a diamond.

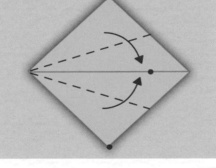

4 Fold the left side under to the right side to make a crease.

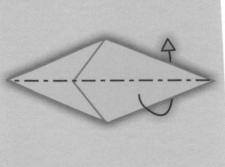

5 Pull the two flaps to open them up slightly.

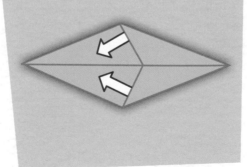

6 Fold the opened top flap down to create a squash fold.

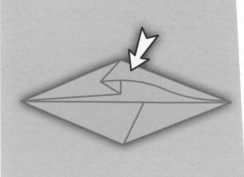

7 Fold the opened bottom flap down to create a squash fold.

8 Fold the bottom half of the shape behind itself along the crease edge.

9 Fold and unfold the middle flap from left to right to make a crease. Repeat on the other side.

10 Fold the middle flap in half to create a leg. Repeat on the other side.

11 Make an outside crimp fold on the left flap to create the neck and head.

12 Make an outside crimp fold on the left flap to create the tail.

13 Make a reverse fold on the right tip to create a crest.

14 Decorate with your stickers, adding eyes and markings.

"Roar!"

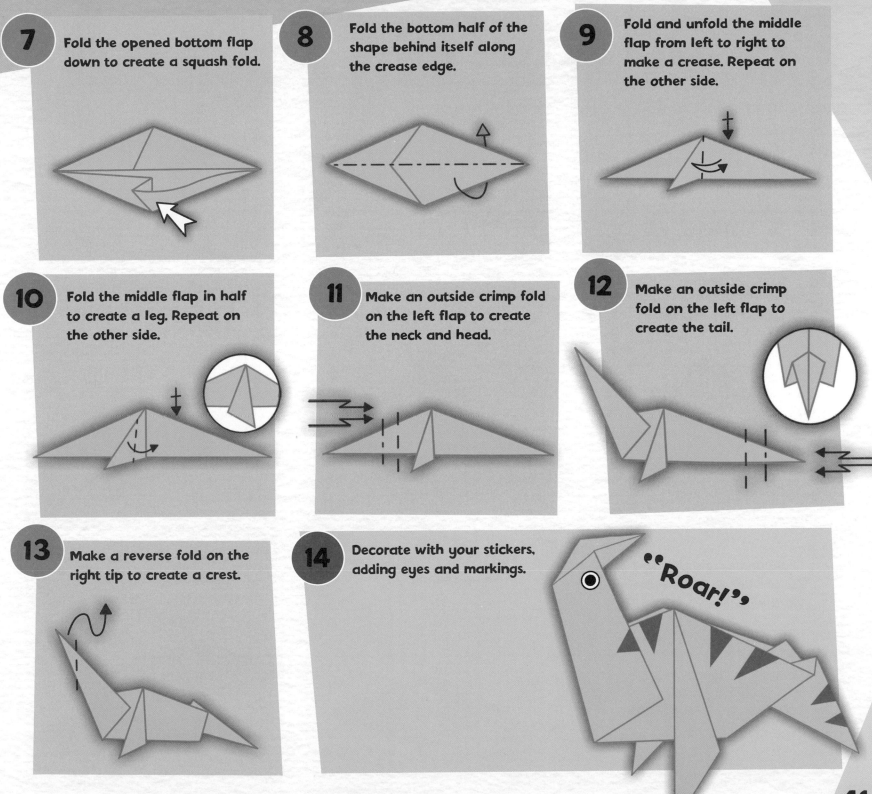

41

Plesiosaurus

Dive straight into the deep end with this underwater wonder!

Medium ⭐ ⭐

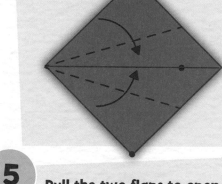

1 Fold and unfold the paper in half to make a crease.

2 Fold the top and bottom points into the middle to make a kite shape.

3 Fold the top and bottom points into the middle, to make a diamond.

4 Fold and unfold the right side to the left to make a crease in the middle.

5 Pull the two flaps to open them up slightly.

6 Fold the opened flaps down to create squash folds on both sides.

7 Fold the bottom half of the shape behind itself.

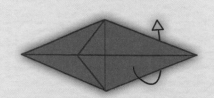

8 Fold and unfold the middle flap from left to right. Repeat on the other side.

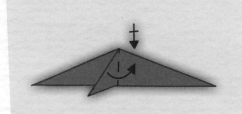

9 Make an inside crimp fold to create the neck.

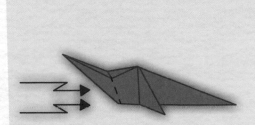

10 Make an inside reverse fold to create the head, as shown in the circle below.

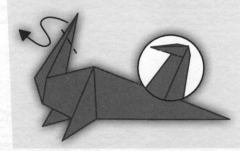

12 Add eyes using the stickers from your sticker sheet!

"splash!"

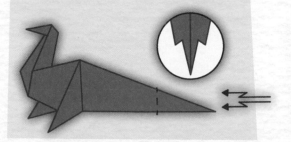

11 Make an inside crimp fold to create the tail.

Pterodactyl

Not every dinosaur roamed the earth...
this one flew!

Hard

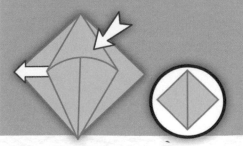

1 Fold the paper in half as shown to create a triangle.

2 Fold the paper in half again from right to left to make a smaller triangle.

3 Rotate the shape then fold and unfold the top left flap to make a crease in the middle.

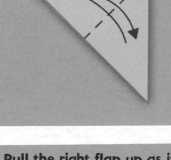

4 Pull the left flap up as if to open, then squash it down so the point meets the bottom right corner (see circle below).

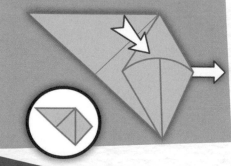

5 Turn the shape over then fold and unfold the top right flap to make a crease.

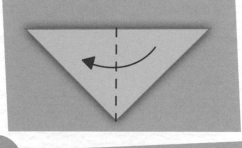

6 Pull the right flap up as if to open, then squash it down so the point meets at the bottom, making a square shape.

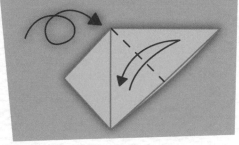

44

7 Rotate the shape 180 degrees. Fold and unfold the left, right and bottom tips into the middle as shown.

8 Pull the top point down and squash the sides of the flap in at the creases made in step 7.

9 Fold the bottom flap up to meet the top point and press to make a crease.

10 There should now be a triangular flap in the middle. Turn the shape over.

11 Fold the upper top flap down and crease.

12 Fold the two flaps down to the sides. These are the wings.

13 Fold the entire shape in half.

14 Make an inside reverse fold as shown to create the head.

15 Decorate with stickers from your sticker sheet!

"Flap, flap!"

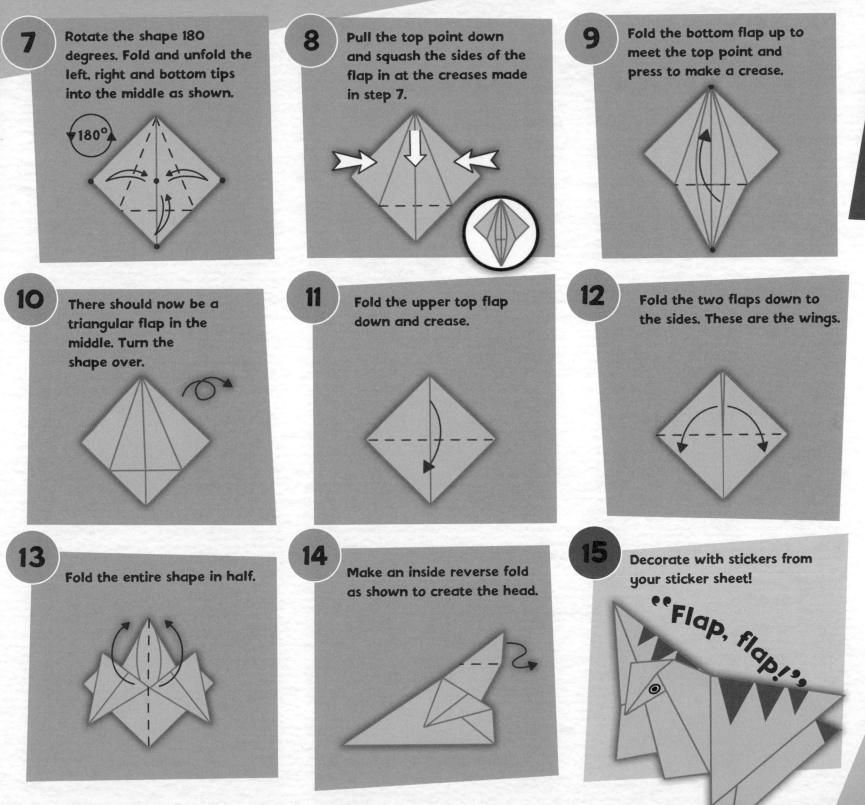

45

Brontosaurus

Was Brontosaurus really just an Apatosaurus?
Let the scientists decide while you fold this fun fellow.

Hard

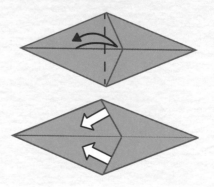

Scissors needed!
Ask an adult to help you

1 Fold the paper in half to make a crease, then fold the points inwards to make a kite shape.

2 Fold the top and the bottom points into the middle to make a diamond.

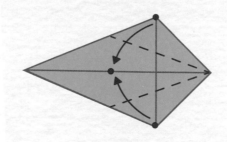

3 Fold the right side to the left to make a middle crease. Then pull the flaps open.

4 Fold the top and bottom flaps down to create a squash fold.

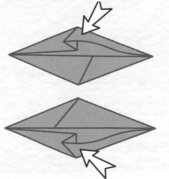

5 Fold the shape behind itself along the crease edge. Fold both side flaps out to make fins.

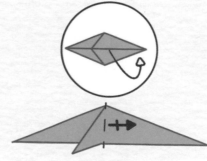

6 Lay the shape flat with the middle flap pointing up. Pull the point downwards to flatten and push in at the sides.

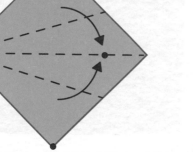

7 Make an outside crimp fold on both sides so the shape is flat along the top.

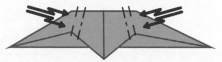

8 Using scissors, carefully cut along the middle crease, stopping before you get to the top. Repeat this on the other side, too.

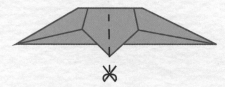

9 Fold the side points to shape the legs. Do this on both sides.

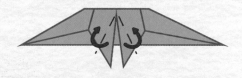

10 Make an inside reverse fold on the left side to form the neck. Make an inside crimp fold on the right side to shape the tail.

12 Decorate your Brontosaurus using the stickers from your sticker sheet. Now she is ready to roam!

"stomp!"

11 Shape the head by making an outside reverse fold.

Velociraptor

Velociraptor was one of the deadliest dinosaurs in history. Make it if you dare!

Medium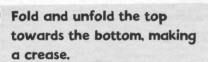

1 Fold and unfold the top towards the bottom, making a crease.

2 Fold the top and bottom points to the middle to make a kite shape.

3 Fold the top and bottom points into the middle to make a diamond shape, then turn the whole thing over.

4 Fold the right point under, then fold the tip back on itself to the right side, making an outside crimp fold.

5 Follow the diagram to make an outside crimp fold on the left side.

6 Make another outside crimp fold on the left side.

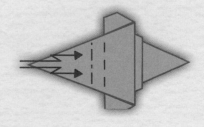

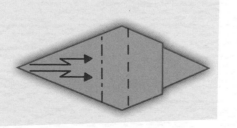

48

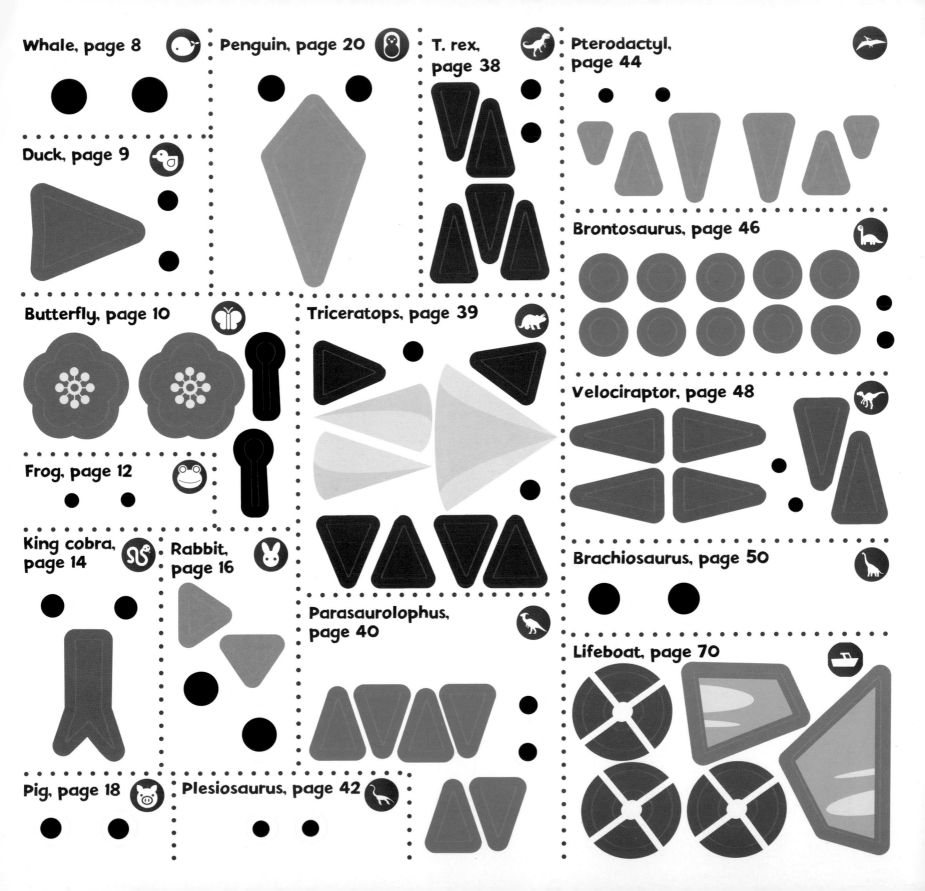

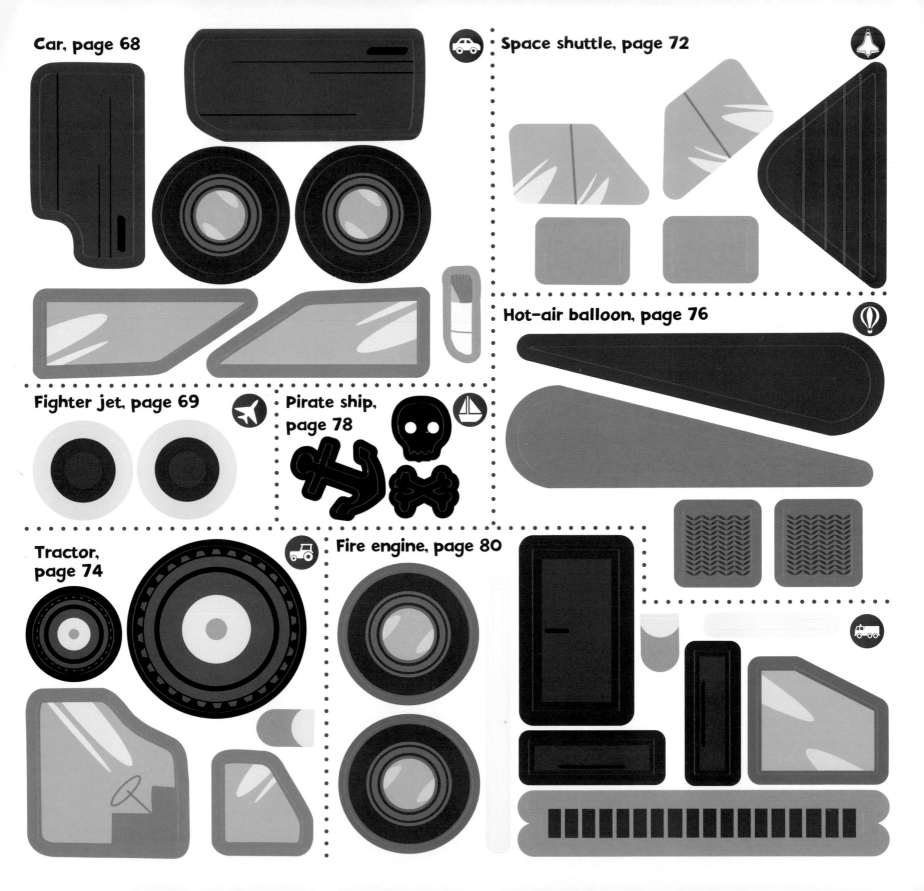

Car, page 68

Space shuttle, page 72

Fighter jet, page 69

Pirate ship, page 78

Hot-air balloon, page 76

Tractor, page 74

Fire engine, page 80

7 Fold the shape up and in half along the main crease edge.

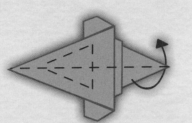

8 Turn the shape 180 degrees.

180°

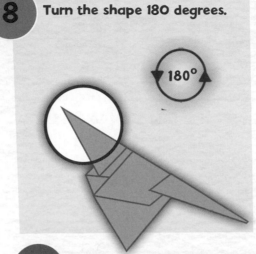

9 To shape the head, fold the top point back and make a crease so that the point is on the left (as in step 10).

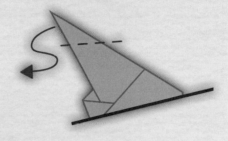

10 Fold the tip to shape the snout.

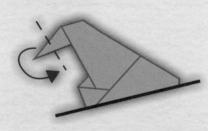

11 Give your Velociraptor a fearsome look by decorating it with the stripes and eyes from your sticker sheet. The other dinosaurs had better watch out!

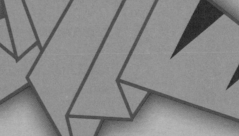

"Boom!"

"Boom!"

"Boom!"

Brachiosaurus

A massive 30m long, Brachiosaurus was one of the largest dinosaurs ever. Make a tiny version with a few simple folds.

Easy ⭐

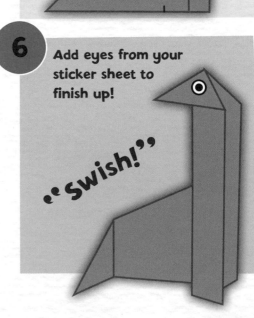

1 Fold the top left point to the right point to make a crease.

2 Fold the straight side of the triangle to the right then over to the left, making a crease. Unfold it.

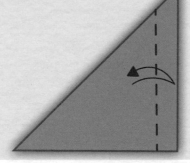

3 Fold the right side to the left again, making a crease that is twice as wide as in step 2.

4 Fold the strip from left to right along the crease, making the neck.

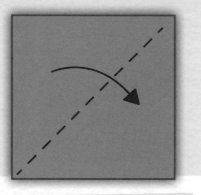

5 Fold the top tip down to the left, making a crease for the head. Fold the bottom left tip inwards to the right, for a tail.

6 Add eyes from your sticker sheet to finish up!

"swish!"

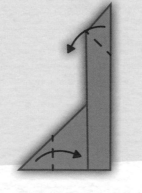

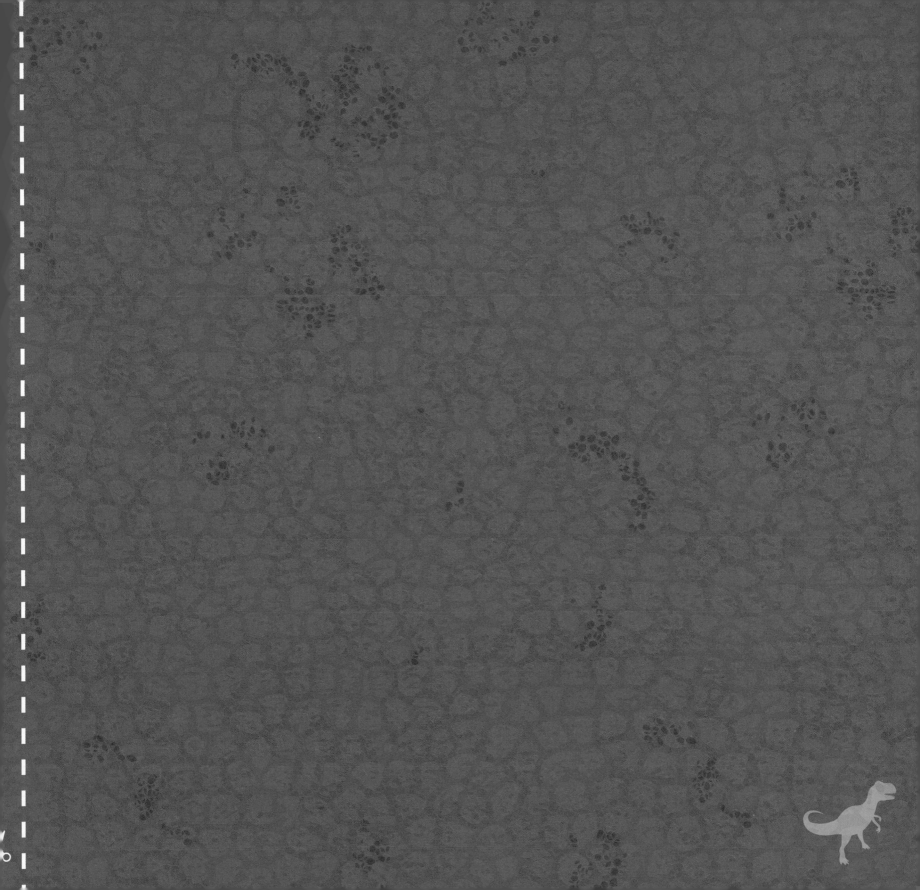

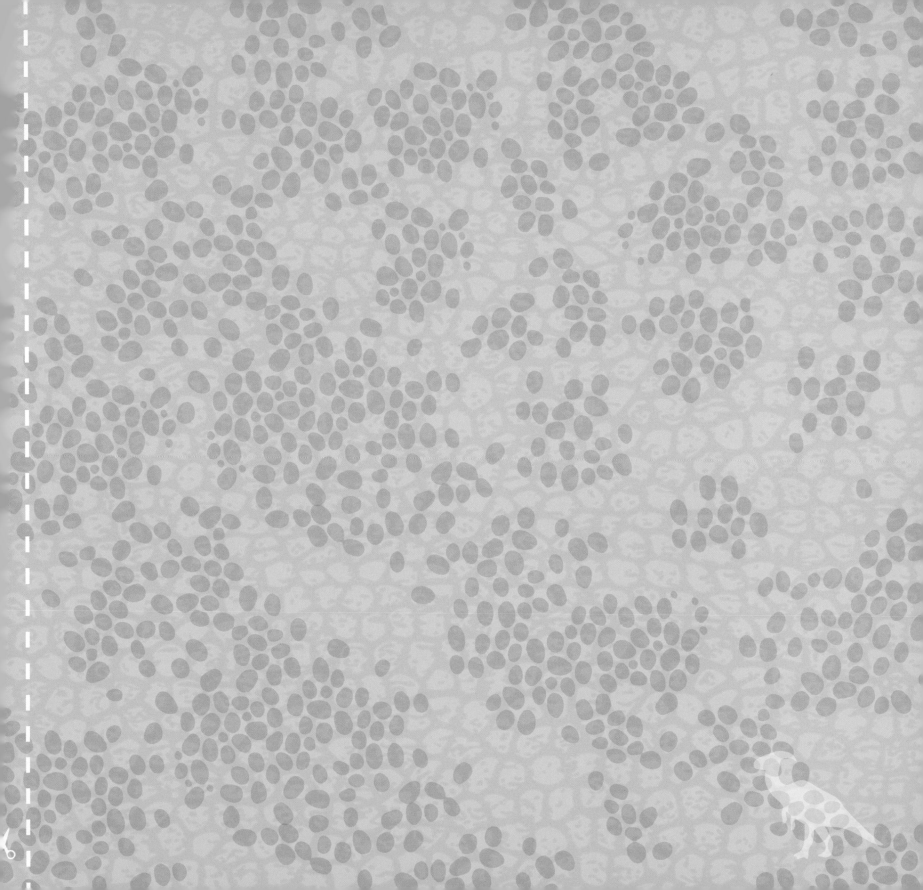

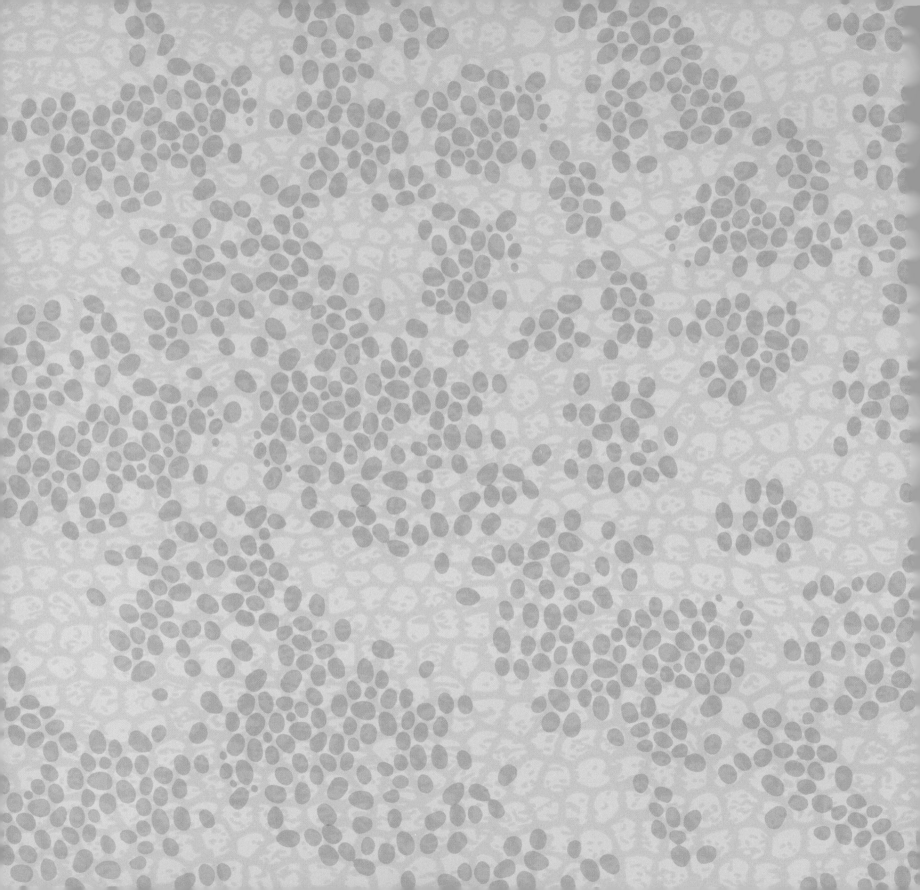

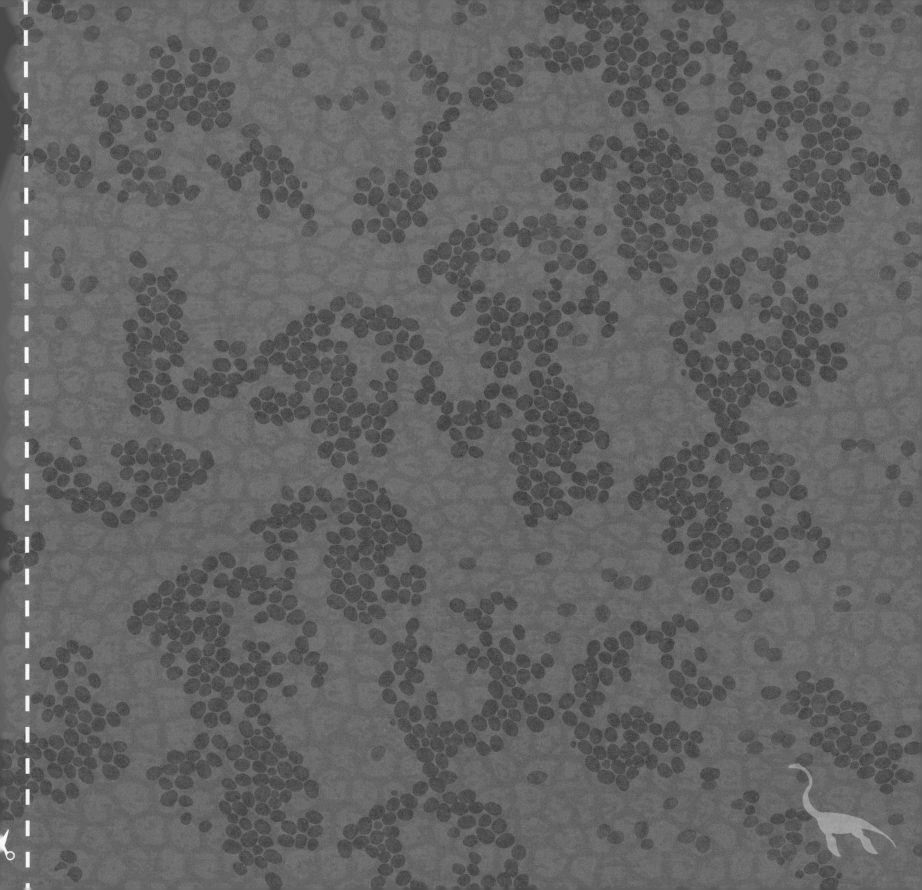

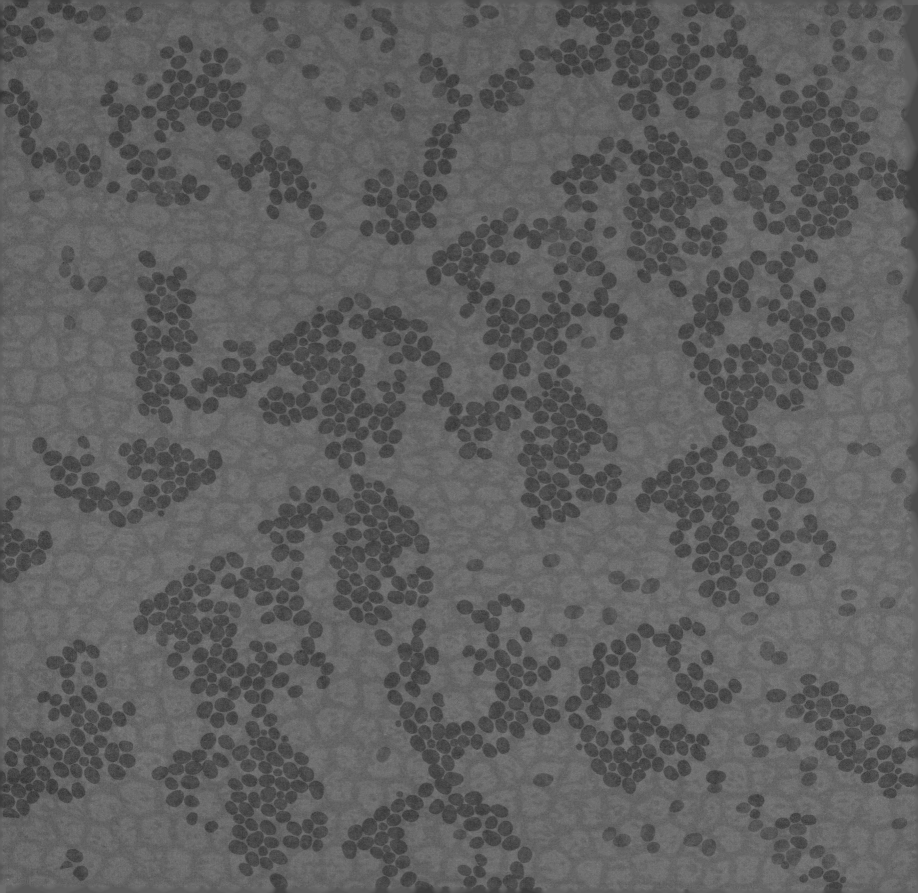

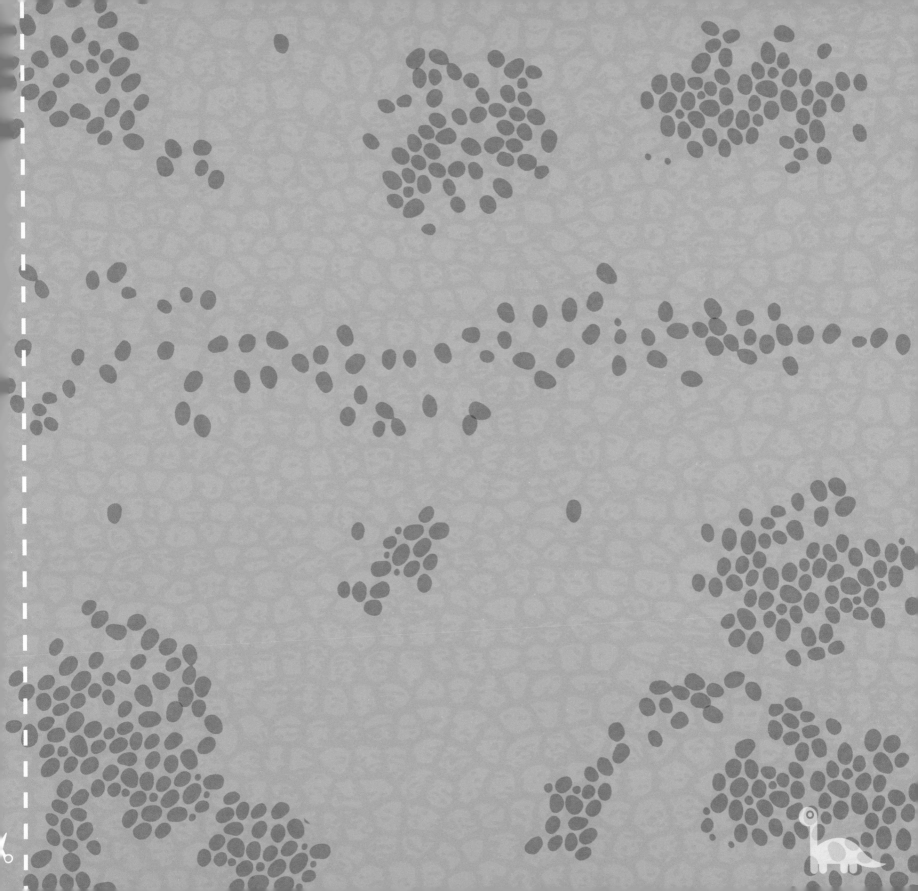

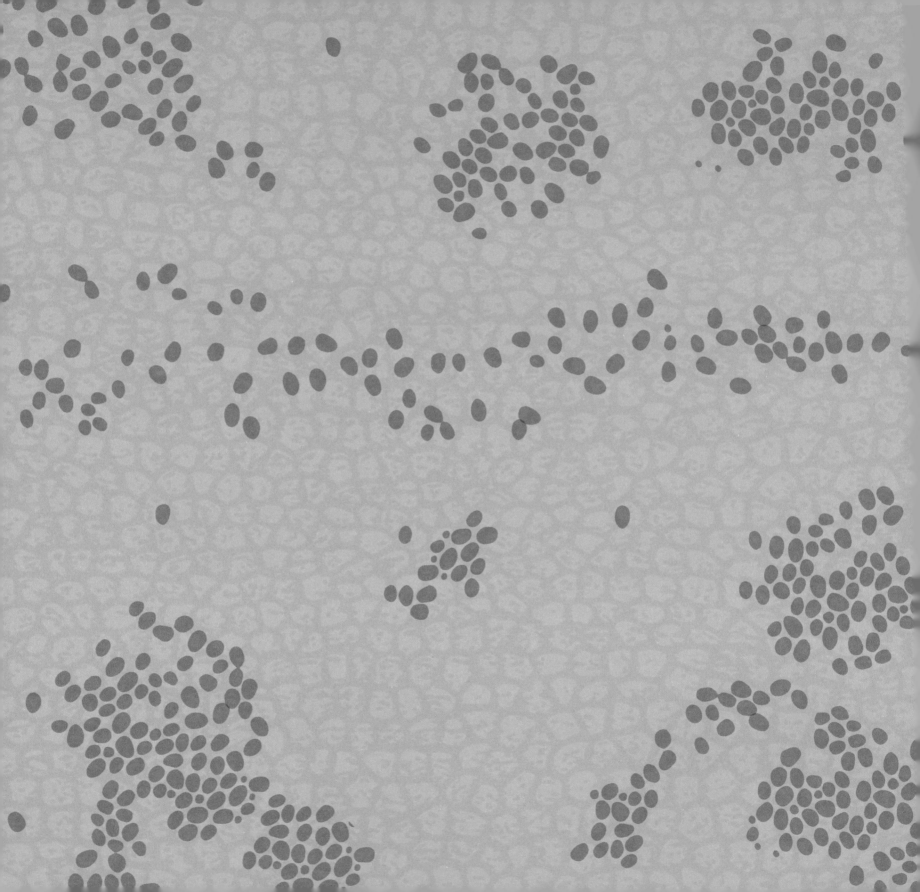

Vehicles

Car

With a few simple folds, you will have your own model car ready to test drive!

Medium ⭐⭐

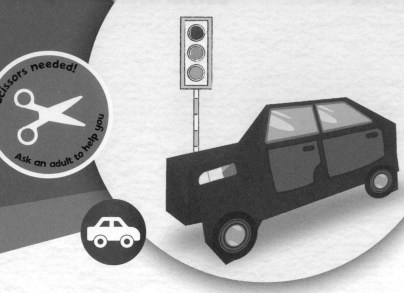

1 Fold and unfold the paper in half to make a crease. Fold the top and bottom edges down by about a third, as shown.

2 Fold the corners downwards to make triangle shapes. The points should come out above the folds, as shown in step 3.

3 Fold the corner tips inwards and press to crease the edge. These will form the wheels.

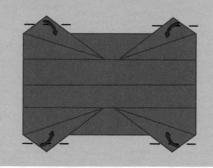

4 Fold the shape in half along the main crease edge. Now make an inside reverse fold to shape the back end.

5 About a quarter of the way in from the straight side of the shape, draw a diagonal line down to the middle. Using scissors, carefully cut along it. Fold the shape inwards, creating a horizontal crease.

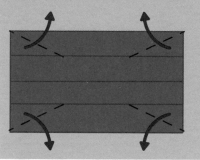

6 Decorate your car with stickers from your sticker sheet then take it for a spin!

"Beep!"

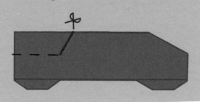

Fighter jet

Test your folding and flying skills with this supersonic plane.

Easy

1 Fold and unfold the paper in half to make a crease.

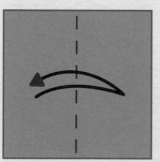

2 Fold the top points to the middle and press to make a crease.

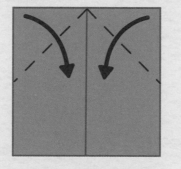

3 Fold both sides down towards the middle.

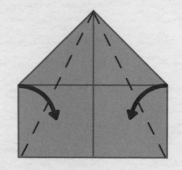

4 Fold the shape in half along the main crease edge.

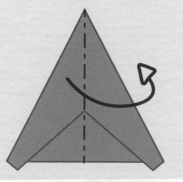

5 Fold the top flap down and press to make a crease as shown in the picture. Then do the same on the other side.

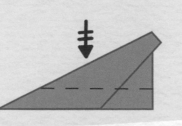

6 Decorate with stickers from your sticker sheet, then prepare to take flight!

"Zoom!"

69

Lifeboat

Heroes needed! Save a life with this brilliant origami boat.

Medium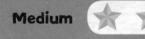

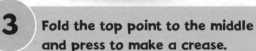
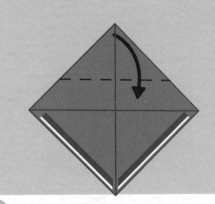

1 Fold and unfold the paper in half from top to bottom, making a crease.

2 Fold and unfold the paper from left to right, pressing down to make a crease.

3 Fold the top point to the middle and press to make a crease.

4 Fold the point back to the top about halfway and press to make a crease.

5 Now fold the top point forward and press to make a crease. See the circle for how it should look.

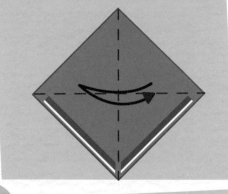

6 Fold the shape in half from left to right along the main crease.

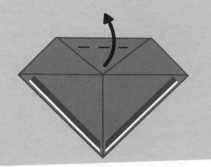

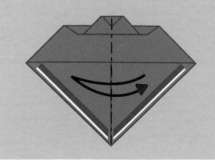

7 Your paper should now look like this.

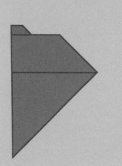

8 Make an outside reverse fold by folding along the dotted edge.

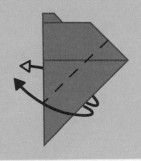

9 Then open the flaps upwards on either side and fold them up so that the point at the front is turned up.

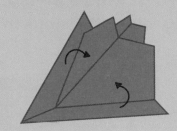

10 Your shape should look like this. Turn it 90 degrees.

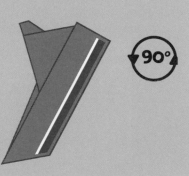

11 To make the lifeboat stand up, fold the back-end flaps inwards. See the circle for how it should look.

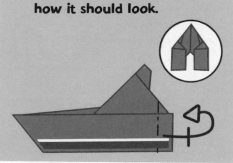

12 Make your boat rescue-ready by decorating it with stickers from your sticker sheet.

"Ready for action!"

Space shuttle

This model will be perfect for a mission to Mars!
Simply follow the steps to countdown.

Medium ⭐ ⭐

Scissors needed! Ask an adult to help you

1 Fold and unfold the paper from left to right, pressing down to make a crease.

2 Fold and unfold the paper from top to bottom, pressing down to make a crease.

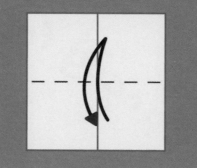

3 Fold the top edge to the middle, pressing down to make a crease.

4 Turn the paper over.

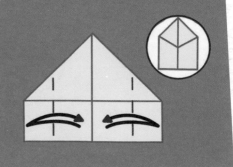

5 Fold both corners in to the middle and press to make a diagonal crease.

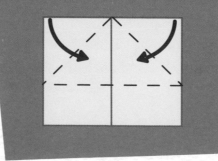

6 Fold and unfold both sides into the middle. See the circle for how it should look.

7 On the left side, make an outside crimp fold. Do this on the right side too. These will form the wings.

8 Using scissors, carefully cut a little way towards the middle crease on the bottom edge.

9 Fold the snipped edges up to the corner points. See the circle for how it should look.

10 Turn the shape over.

11 Fold the left-side edge up, making a wing tip. Repeat on the right side.

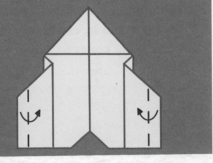

12 Decorate with stickers from your sticker sheet, then have an awesome, astronomical adventure.

"Blast off!"

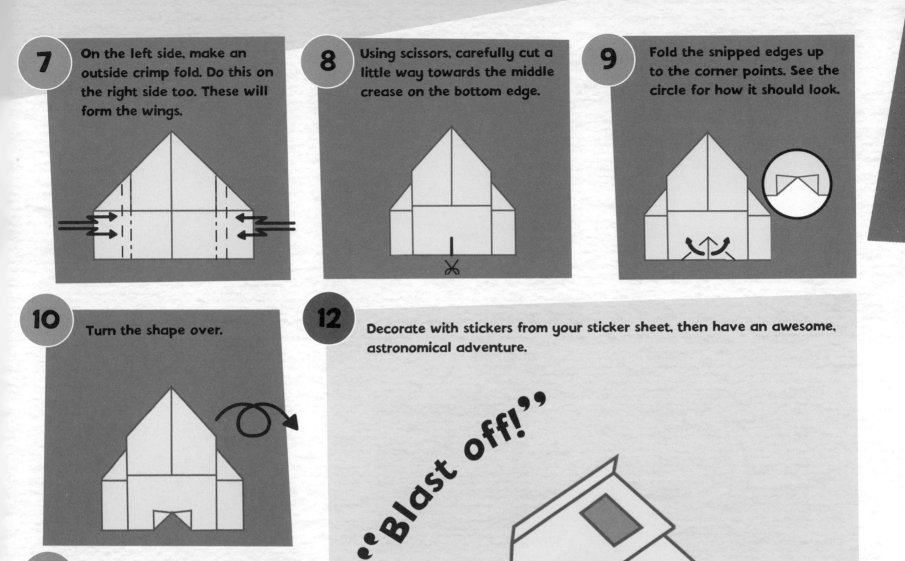

Tractor

This farm fave won't make your hands mucky, but it will keep them busy!

Hard ⭐⭐⭐

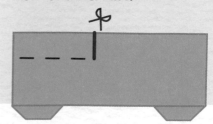

1 Fold the paper in half from top to bottom, making a crease, then unfold.

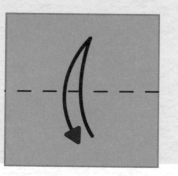

2 Fold the top and bottom edges down about a third, as shown.

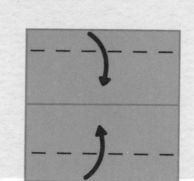

3 Fold the corners into triangle shapes so the points come above the folds.

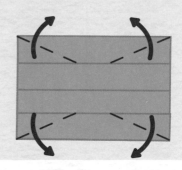

4 Fold the corner tips inwards and press to crease the edges. These will form the wheels.

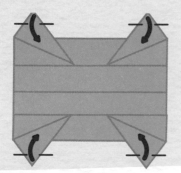

5 Fold the shape in half along the main crease.

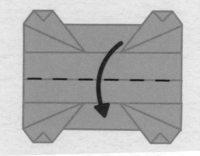

6 About a quarter of the way from the left side of the shape, draw a straight line down to the middle. Use scissors to carefully cut along it. Fold the shape inwards, creating a horizontal crease.

7 Open the shape out.

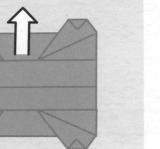

8 With the shape open, make an accordion fold to the right.

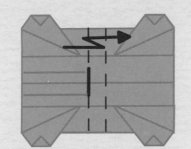

9 Fold the shape in half back down along the crease edge.

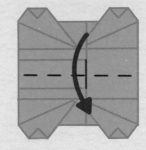

10 Make an inside reverse fold on the left by pushing the tip up and pressing the sides together.

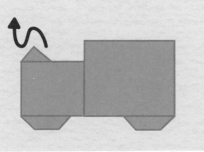

11 Make an inside reverse fold at the tip of the funnel, and at the top right corner of the tractor.

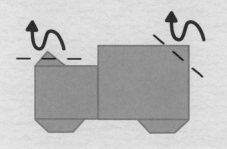

12 Decorate your tractor with the stickers from your sticker sheet, then get to work down on the farm!

"chug, chug!"

Hot-air balloon

See the world from a whole new view with this cloud-sweeping hot-air balloon.

Medium ⭐ ⭐

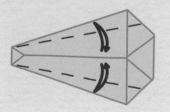

1 Fold and unfold the square in half from left to right, making a crease.

2 Fold and unfold the square from top to bottom, making a crease.

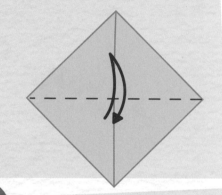

3 Fold the top and bottom points into the middle to make a kite shape.

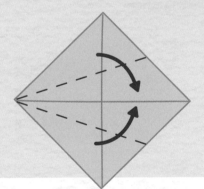

4 Fold the right-hand point into the middle.

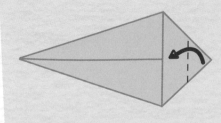

5 Fold the left-hand point inwards. See the circle for how it should look.

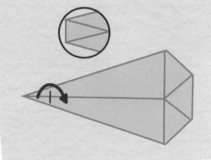

6 Fold and unfold the top and bottom sides down, making creases.

7 Fold the left side in, making an accordion fold.

8 Turn the shape anticlockwise by 90 degrees, so it is upright.

90°

9 At the bottom of the shape, fold up the end to form the basket.

10 Fold and unfold the shape from right to the left along the main crease.

11 Use stickers from your sticker sheet to decorate the balloon, then prepare to take flight!

"UP, up and away!"

Pirate ship

Ahoy there shipmate, master this and maybe you won't walk the plank!

Medium ⭐ ⭐

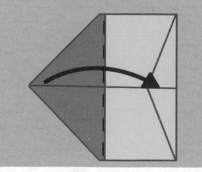

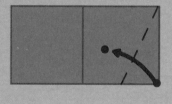

1 Fold and unfold the square in half from left to right, making a crease.

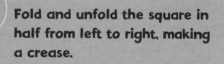

2 Fold the bottom edge up towards the top, making a rectangle shape.

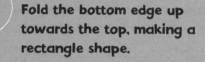

3 Fold the bottom right corner up as shown.

4 Open the shape up.

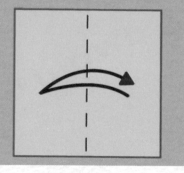

5 Fold the top left corner in to the middle. Then do the same with the bottom left corner.

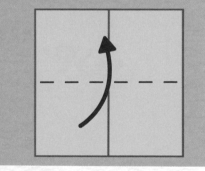

6 Fold the left-hand side over, so the point meets the middle of the right-hand side.

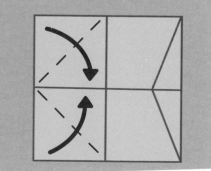

7 Fold the bottom edge underneath, creating a diamond shape.

8 Turn your shape 45 degrees so the main triangle shape is pointing downwards. Take the right edge and push it inwards to form a sail.

9 Fold the bottom point upwards, along the crease.

10 Push the flap inside the bottom of the boat to help the pirate ship stand up.

14 Decorate your ship with stickers from your sticker sheet, then set sail!

"yo-ho-ho!"

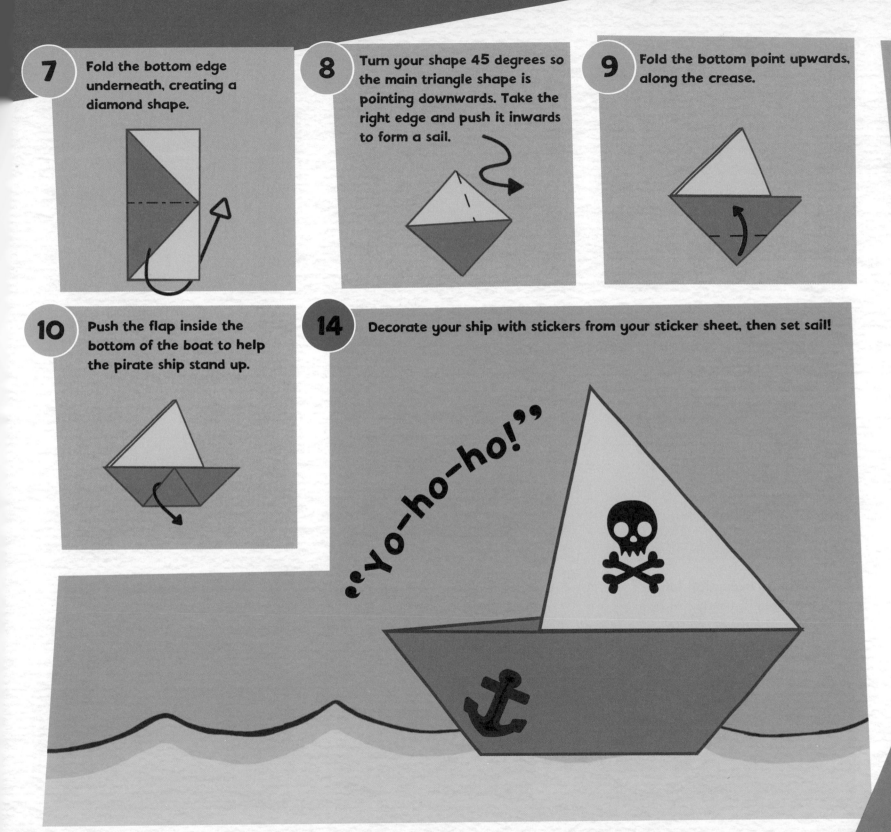

Fire engine

Race to the rescue with this blazingly fast red appliance!

Easy ⭐

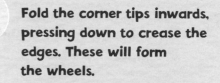

1 Fold and unfold the paper in half, making a crease. Fold the top and bottom edges down about a third.

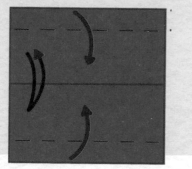

2 Fold the corners into triangle shapes so the points are above the folds.

3 Fold the corner tips inwards, pressing down to crease the edges. These will form the wheels.

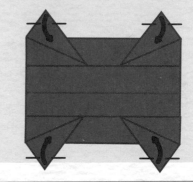

4 Make an accordion fold, then fold the shape in half along the main crease.

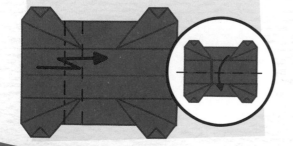

5 Make an inside reverse fold in the top left corner to shape the fire engine cab.

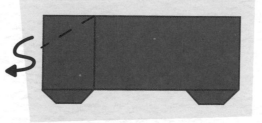

6 Decorate with stickers from your sticker sheet.

"Nee-naw!"

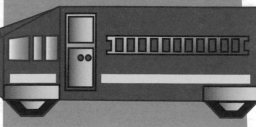